THE CHRONICLES OF JUDGE DREDD by John Wagner, Alan Grant and Cliff Robinson

JUDGE DREDD 18

INTRODUCTION

I first saw Brian Bolland's art work in the offices of *2000AD*. He was one of the first Judge Dredd artists, whose work appeared in Judge Dredd Book One. I was amazed that all his work was inked with a brush. At that time my drawing was poor, to say the least, and I felt Brian's finishing method could carry my weak drawing until I could originate my own style. I didn't want to spend years in my artist's garrett developing my own inking technique and eventually dying of consumption! I wanted to get in there and learn on the job. As a kid I was weaned on Marvel and DC Comics, so I had to gear my style toward *2000AD* as I went along. The following notes are just some of my memories of working on the stories collected in this volume.

The Ugly Bug Ball — (Prog 447). A weird story with many weird faces. When I draw vehicles, I try to draw them futuristically and the look of futuristic films like *Blade Runner* influence me quite a lot. However, tight deadlines mean that occasionally I have to use contemporary vehicles for reference.

West Side Rumble — (Prog 434). There's a lot of violence in this story, and I think there's a fine line between cartoon violence and commiting actual violence. I saw violence when I was a kid, and I didn't grow up to be a mass murderer. I've only killed a couple of people, so that's not mass murder. Is it?

Zombie Barbecue — (Prog 470). In some ways this is quite like a story from Will Eisner's classic crime series *The Spirit*, in that it's about the city, and about how its citizens live, think and feel. Judge Dredd is just a secondary character. I liked the touching quality of the story.

Crippen and Turk — (Prog 489). Quite witty of Wagner and Grant to have the rival blocks named after the two members of *Wham!* This is the story where I started to develop the idea of drawing horizontal lines across the facial features of each character, which I feel is my first shy step towards a style of my own.

Chief Judge Resigns — (Prog 457). No matter who is in power, the social conditions remain the same. The two tramps were modelled facially on two of my friends.

Beware the Booby Prize — (1984 Summer Special). My first Dredd story, my first ten-pager and, frankly, I wasn't ready for it. Previous to this my only professional work had been two *Future Shock* stories for *2000AD*, and I didn't have much confidence in my work. I think that, here, it was a case of bad drawing saved by Bolland-style inking.

A Real Christmas Story — (Prog 502). This story shows the complete power that writers have over their characters and the way they can play around with them. In it, the main characters are turned into uglies, then raving psychos, killed and finally resurrected for a happy ending!! By the end of the story I was sick of drawing snowflakes. Also, there's a self-portrait in here: in the panel with the nutter, I'm the handsome brute with the classy glasses looking over the nutter's shoulder.

To conclude, I hope you enjoy the art that illustrates the stories in this book. I'm not satisfied with it and I'm always trying to improve. I enjoy working on the *Dredd* strip; but drawing the seven-link chain on Judge Dredd's chest is slowly driving me mad!

'Nuff Said?

Cliff Robinson, *August 1987*.

JOHN WAGNER was largely responsible, along with Pat Mills, for the renaissance of British comics in the 1970s and the creation of Battle, Action *and* 2000 AD. *He has scripted* Strontium Dog, Robo-Hunter *and* Judge Dredd *under his pseudonyms and is currently working with Alan Grant, co-writing* Judge Dredd *for IPC and* The Outcasts *for DC Comics. He is also developing* The Last American, *with Mike McMahon for Marvel's Epic Comics line.*

ALAN GRANT began his comics career in 1977, writing Tarzan *for European publication. After a year as sub-editor on 2000 AD he went freelance, and since 1980 has worked in partnership with John Wagner. Current stories include:* Judge Dredd, Strontium Dog *and* Ace Trucking Co *for 2000 AD;* Kaleb Daark, *with Brett Ewins, for Citadel Miniatures;* Outcasts *with Cam Kennedy, for D.C.;* The Last American, *with Mike McMahon, for Epic.*

CLIFF ROBINSON studied graphic design at Great Yarmouth College of Art and Design from 1979 to 1981. His first published work appeared in a local newspaper in 1982. Introduced to IPC's 2000 AD *by Robin Smith, he began by drawing* Future-Shocks *in 1983. Eventually he moved on to draw* Judge Dredd, *which he continues to draw till the present day.*

Published by Titan Books Ltd, 58 St Giles High St, London WC2H 8LH, England. Distributed in the United Kingdom and the United States of America by Titan Distributors Ltd, P.O. Box 250, London E3 4RT, England. Printed in England. ISBN 1 85286 003 0. *First edition October 1987.*

10 9 8 7 6 5 4 3 2 1

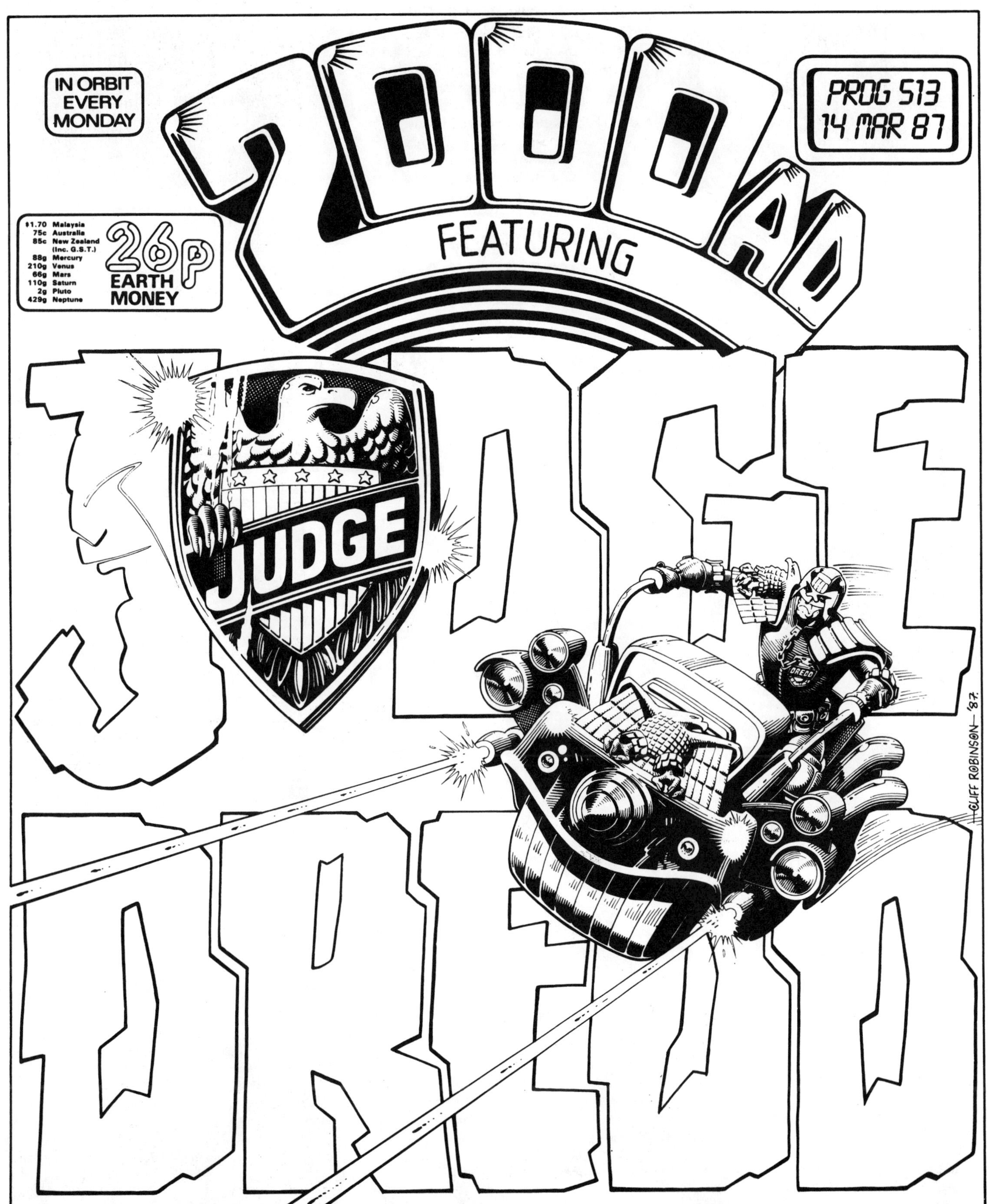
IN ORBIT EVERY MONDAY
2000 AD
PROG 513
14 MAR 87
FEATURING
$1.70 Malaysia
75c Australia
85c New Zealand (Inc. G.S.T.)
88g Mercury
210g Venus
66g Mars
110g Saturn
2g Pluto
429g Neptune
26p EARTH MONEY
JUDGE
JUDGE DREDD
DREDD
CLIFF ROBINSON '87.

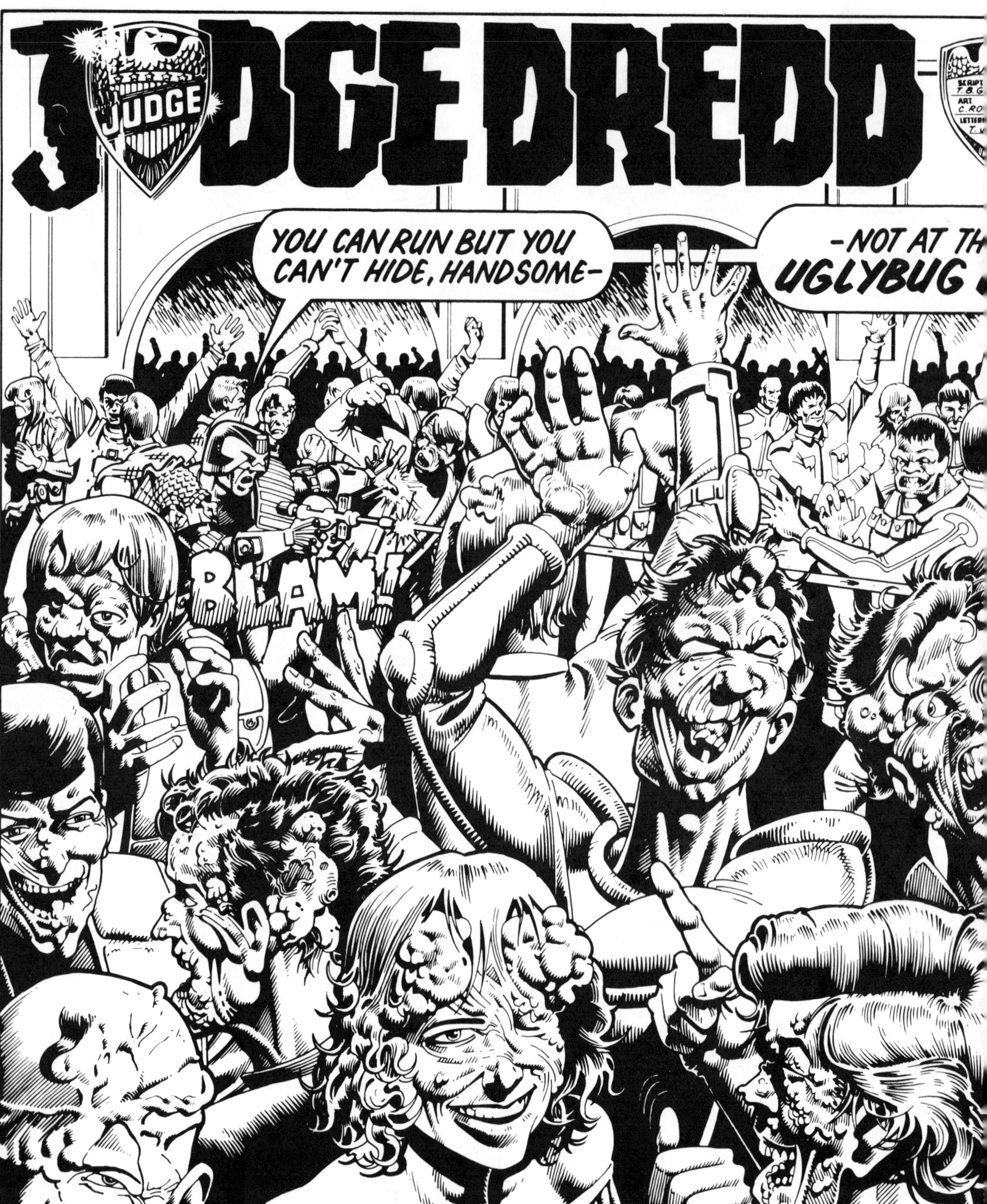
JUDGE DREDD
JUDGE
YOU CAN RUN BUT YOU CAN'T HIDE, HANDSOME-
-NOT AT TH
UGLYBUG
BLAM!

JUDGES HAVE THROWN A CORDON AROUND SECTOR 140'S FOLLY HEIGHTS —
WHERE YOU IDIOTS GOING—A FREAK SHOW?

YOU BET! WE'RE OFF TO THE UGLYBUG BALL!

OKAY, MOVE ON. AND KEEP YOUR EYES OPEN. THERE'S AN ESCAPED CON ON THE LOOSE.
YOUNG? FUN LOVING? UGLY? THEN BE THERE AT THE UGLYBUG BALL TONITE
JUDGES SWARMING ALL OVER THE PLACE... BUT THEY'RE NOT GOING TO STOP ME GETTING TO YOU, HOWIE.

RECKON RANSOM WILL SHOW?
BOUND TO. HOWIE BUCK'S INFORMATION SENT HIM DOWN FOR THIRTY. RANSOM'S NOT THE KIND OF CREEP TO FORGET THAT.

HEY, JUDGE—DULT BACK IN THE ALLEY GAVE ME FIFTY CREDS TO GIVE THIS TO YOU.
EH?

GET RID OF IT!

SO LONG, HOWIE!
VADOOOOM!

DREDD! RANSOM'S GOT THROUGH! HALF THE STREET'S GONE UP— BUCK'S BLOCK WITH IT!

I SEE IT! ON MY WAY!

VRMMM!
RANSOM KNOWS HIS GETAWAY WILL NOT BE EASY. BUT HE HAS ALWAYS BEEN RECKLESS WITH HIS LIFE—

SPLAT!
AAAGH!
AND EVEN MORE RECKLESS WITH THE LIVES OF OTHERS!

THERE HE IS!
BLAM!
UGLYBUG BALL

UNHH—

HERE AT THE UGLYBUG BALL I'M SPEAKING TO GLENDON GROTT.
GLEN—YOU'RE THE FACE THAT MAKES THE PACE. LIKE TO SAY WHY?

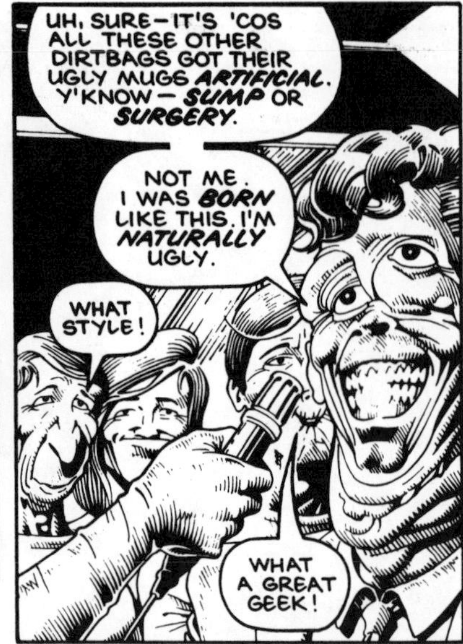
UH, SURE—IT'S 'COS ALL THESE OTHER DIRTBAGS GOT THEIR UGLY MUGG ARTIFICIAL. Y'KNOW—SUMP OR SURGERY.
NOT ME. I WAS BORN LIKE THIS. I'M NATURALLY UGLY.
WHAT STYLE!
WHAT A GREAT GEEK!

LOOK OUT!
SCREEEEE!

AND HERE'S A NEW ARRIVAL! YOUR NAME, SIR—
SHUT YOUR STUPID MOUTH!

CLEAR THE WAY!

SHAKE YOUR WARTS, BABY!
ZOOP DE ZOOP!
DRANG—THE FACES!

HEY! GET A LOADA HAND-SOME!
GET LOST, PRETTY BOY!
WE DON'T WANT YOUR TYPE ROUND HERE!
WHAT KIND OF MADHOUSE IS THIS?

RANSOM HAD BEEN AWAY A LONG TIME — LONG BEFORE THE "UGLY" CRAZE HAD TAKEN THE CITY BY STORM —
A NIGHTMARE! IT'S GOTTA BE A NIGHTMARE!

YOU CAN'T HIDE IN THIS LOT, RANSOM!
URGGGH!

KEEP BACK, LAWMAN, OR I'LL BLOW THIS LITTLE BEAUTY AWAY!
1st PRIZE
GOT TO GET WITHIN STRIKING RANGE —

GO RIGHT AHEAD.
EH?
I MEAN WHAT I SAY!

SO DO I. FACE LIKE THAT, YOU'D BE DOING HER A FAVOUR.

AHHHHHHH!
NOW!

UGGGGH!

1st PRIZE
ONE YEARS SUPPLY
OF
OTTO SUMP UGLY
PRODUCTS
SQUIRT!
SPLAT!
SQUELCH!

AHHH! GET IT OFF! IT'S BURNING!

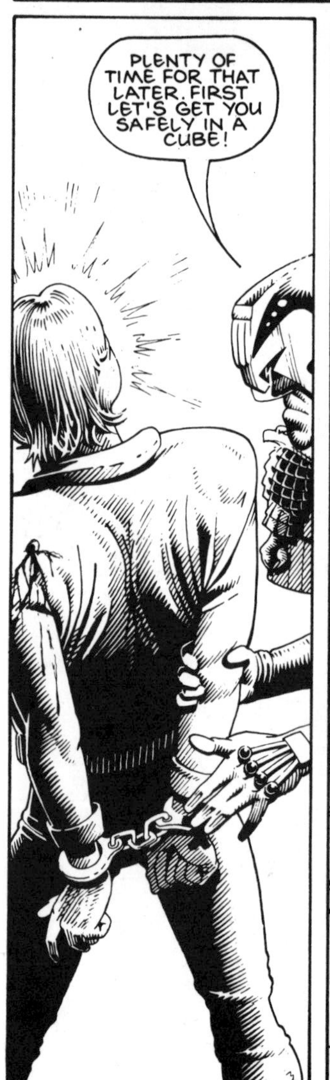
PLENTY OF TIME FOR THAT LATER. FIRST LET'S GET YOU SAFELY IN A CUBE!

EXIT
CARRY ON WITH THE FREAK SHOW, FOLKS!
AT THE SECTOR HOUSE—
THE "UGLY" PREPARATIONS HAVE MADE A BIT OF A MESS OF HIM, DREDD. YOU WANT HIM SCHEDULED FOR FACE CHANGE SURGERY?
SURE. BUT DON'T RUSH IT.
RANSOM COMMITTED SOME PRETTY UGLY CRIMES. LET'S SEE HOW HE LIKES LIVING WITH HIMSELF FOR A WHILE!
NEXT PROG: A DAY AT THE BLOCK WARS!

PROG 434

7 SEP 85

WEST SIDE RUMBLE

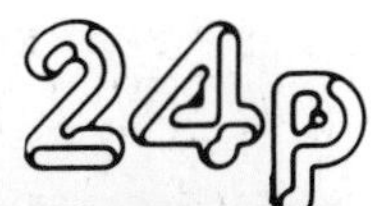

$1.45 Malaysia 65c Australia 65c New Zealand

IN ORBIT EVERY MONDAY

2000 AD FEATURING JUDGE DREDD

SHARKS

A-RUMBLING! A-RUMBLING!

THE SHARKS WERE BORN FOR RUMBLING!

THERE'S NOTHIN' WE LIKE BETTER THAN A FIGHT!

JUDGE DREDD
JUDGE
WEST SIDE RUMBLE
THEY'D BEEN WAITING THERE SINCE NIGHTFALL FOR THE SHARKS TO COME ALONG, THEY KNEW THEY'D HAVE TO PASS THIS STRETCH OF STREET. SO THEY'D SHARPENED UP THEIR STICKERS AND THEY'D BROUGHT ALONG THEIR BARS, AND THEY WERE WEARING STEEL-TIPPED STOMPERS ON THEIR FEET.
THERE WAS BIG FRANK ZIT AND FACEACHE, CRAZY JOSEPH WITH HIS SPEAR, THE DIXON BOYS WERE THERE AND BILLY RAT. IKE THE SPIKE HAD BROUGHT HIS SISTER WITH HER HOMEMADE GHETTO BLASTER, AND THE GHOUL HAD PUT NEW RIVETS IN HIS BAT.
SCRIPT T B GROVER
ART CLIFF ROBINSON
LETTERING T FRAME

NOW IT WASN'T NOTHIN' PERSONAL THAT THEY HAD AGAINST THE SHARKS,
ANY BUNCH OF DEAD-END SPUGS WOULD DO.
'COS THERE WAS NOTHING THEY LIKED BETTER THAN TO MASH AND BASH AND STOMP,
SAME AS ANY NORMAL MEGA-CITY JUVES.
THE ZITS!
A-RUMBLING! A-RUMBLING! WE LOVE TO GO A-RUMBLING!
WE LOVE TO LAY IN AMBUSH IN THE NIGHT!
A-RUMBLING! A-RUMBLING! THE ZITS WERE BORN FOR RUMBLING!
THERE'S NOTHING WE LIKE BETTER THAN A FIGHT!
AAAH!
AAAAA!
SMAK!
KRAK!
THEN A HEADLIGHT PIERCED THE DARKNESS — A RIDER GAUNT AND GRIM,
DAYSTICK DRAWN AND READY IN HIS HAND.
THE CHIN BELONGED TO DREDD,
AND THE VOICE AS WELL, WHICH SAID:
YOU CREEPS CAN DO YOUR RUMBLING IN THE CAN!

"IT'S JUST ONE JUDGE!" CRIED CINDY SPIKE AND OPENED WITH HER BLASTER –
I'LL SEND HIM BACK TO CENTRAL IN A SACK!
SPOING!
AAAAAAA!
BUT DREDD'S BIKE ABSORBED THE BLAST AND HE LAID HER ON THE STREET,
WITH TYRE MARKS RUNNING RIGHT ACROSS HER BACK.
THEN THE JUDGE GOT DOWN TO BUSINESS AND HIS DAYSTICK ROSE AND FELL, STRIKING OUT AT EVERY HEAD HE SAW.
ZITS
DREDD
FOR THOUGH THE ZITS LAUNCHED THE ATTACK, THE SHARKS WERE FIGHTING BACK –
SHARK
ZITS
AND SELF DEFENCE IS NO DEFENCE IN LAW!

AS THE HEAP OF BODIES MOUNTED, BIG ZIT COULD SEE HIS WATERLOO, WAITING JUST ONE STATION DOWN THE LINE.
OH, SURE, HE LOVED TO RUMBLE – BUT HE PREFERRED TO BE ON TOP...
LET'S SCRAM AND LIVE TO FIGHT ANOTHER TIME!
DREDD TO CONTROL! WE GOT FORTY-PLUS JUVE RUMBLERS FLEEING EAST THROUGH BERNSTEIN. ZITS AND SHARKS. BACK-UP REQUIRED.
WILCO, DREDD!
MED SQUADS AND MEAT WAGONS TO MORENO ALLEY.
ESTIMATE TWENTY CASUALTIES. MORE TO FOLLOW.
ZITS
VRMMMM!
CONTROL TO ALL UNITS AREA BERNSTEIN. YPs ON THE RUN.
PICK 'EM UP!
VRMMM
IN THE SPACE OF SIXTY SECONDS THERE WAS A JUDGE ON EVERY STREET. FROM WATCHING BAYS OTHERS SCANNED THE SLAB –
WE GOT TWO ZITS RUNNIN' FAST THROUGH THE TAMBLIN UNDERPASS!
NUGENT
KRUPKE HERE! I GOT 'EM IN THE BAG!

THUNK!
THUNK!
ZITS

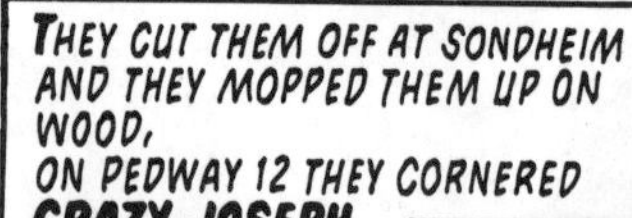
THEY CUT THEM OFF AT SONDHEIM AND THEY MOPPED THEM UP ON WOOD,
ON PEDWAY 12 THEY CORNERED **CRAZY JOSEPH**.

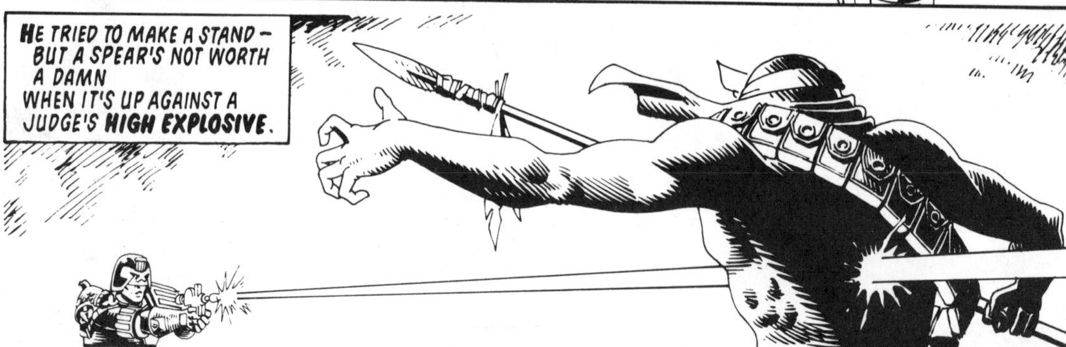
HE TRIED TO MAKE A STAND – BUT A SPEAR'S NOT WORTH A DAMN WHEN IT'S UP AGAINST A JUDGE'S **HIGH EXPLOSIVE**.

THE **GHOUL** SURRENDERED QUIETLY, HE DIDN'T HAVE MUCH CHOICE –

IKE THE SPIKE TRIED TO SCALE THE SECTOR WALL –
SAVE YOUR BULLET. HE'LL NEVER MAKE IT.

OH NO!

AAAAAAAAAHH!
SPLATT!
LENNY BERNSTEIN
THE DIXON BOYS ALL COPPED IT WHEN THEY TRIED TO HITCH A RIDE ON THE 2020 ZOOM TO BERNSTEIN HALT.
BIG ZIT THOUGHT HE'D PLAY IT CLEVER, THE LAW WAS EVERYWHERE, THE SAFEST THING FOR HIM TO DO WAS HIDE –
DREDD TRACKED HIM DOWN ON INFRA-RED –
DON'T BOTHER TO COME OUT !
THE BEST PLACE FOR TRASH LIKE YOU IS INSIDE !
YAAAAAA

IN MINUTES FLAT THEY'D CAUGHT THEM, EVERY SHARK AND EVERY ZIT. TO DREDD IT FELL TO LADLE OUT THE YEARS –
TWENTY YEARS APIECE FOR CINDY SPIKE, BILLY RAT AND GHOUL.
AN EXTRA TEN LEFT BIG FRANK ZIT IN TEARS –
THIRTY YEARS, MAN! FOR THAT CRUMMY LITTLE RUMBLE? IT AIN'T FAIR! THERE OUGHTA BE A LAW AGAINST IT!
FOR FACEACHE MINUS HALF HIS FACE, FOR THE HAPLESS DIXON BOYS, FOR IKE IMPALED SO CRUELLY ON HIS SPIKE. FOR CRAZY JOE WITH HIS GAPING HOLE, THERE'D BE ONE FINAL RUMBLE, ALONG THE LAST CONVEYOR BELT AT RESYK.
A-RUMBLING! A-RUMBLING! THEY LOVED TO GO A-RUMBLING! BUT THE ZITS WILL GO A-RUMBLING NO MORE! A-RUMBLING! A-RUMBLING! THEY LOVED TO GO A-RUMBLING!
BUT THEY SHOULD'VE KNOWN THEY COULDN'T BUCK THE LAW!
THE END.

JUSTICE IS IN THE EYE OF THE BEHOLDER!

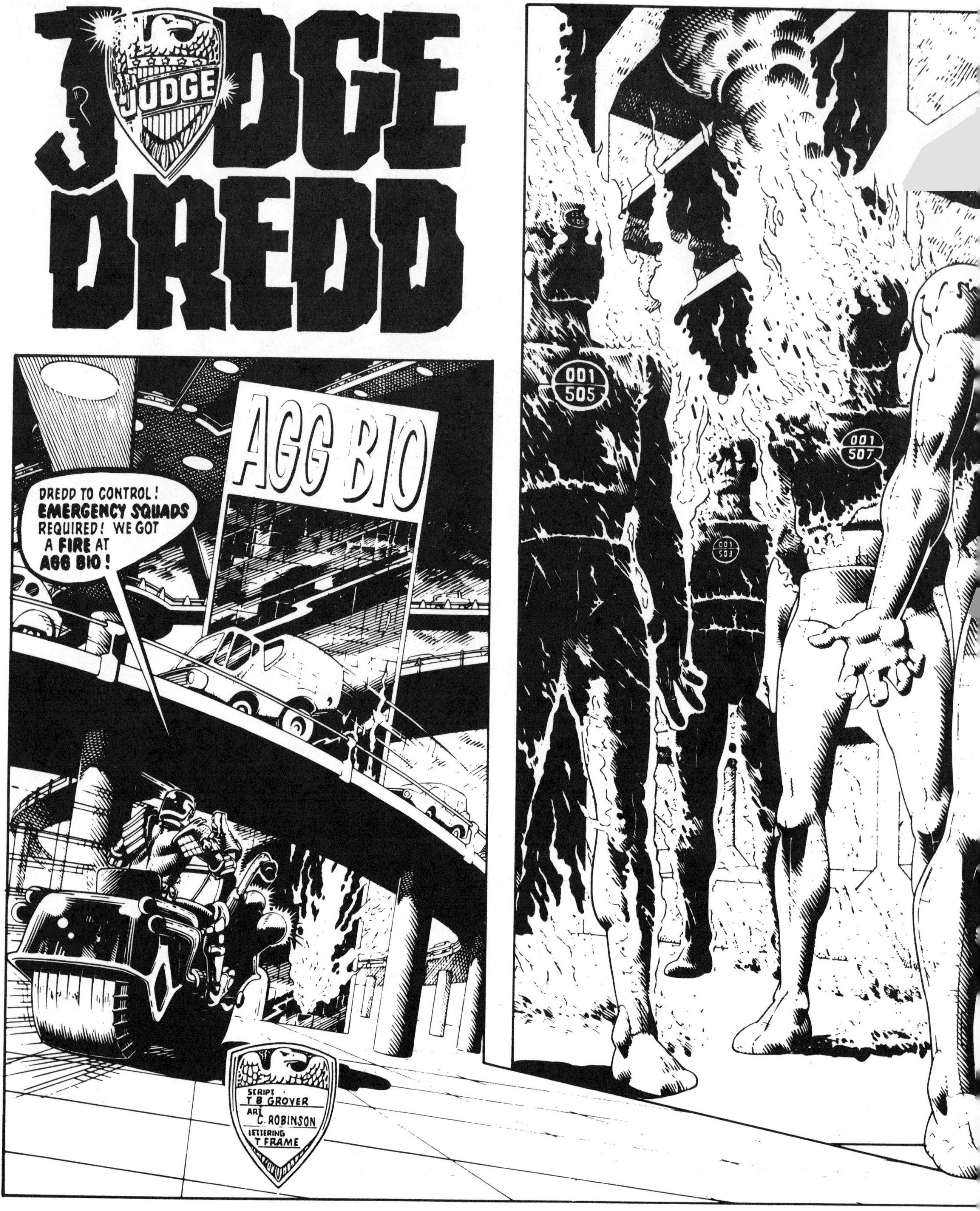

JUDGE DREDD

AGG BIO
DREDD TO CONTROL! EMERGENCY SQUADS REQUIRED! WE GOT A FIRE AT AGG BIO!
SCRIPT T B GROVER
ART C. ROBINSON
LETTERING T FRAME

DROKK! CREEP'S HOLDIN' A ZOMBIE BARBEQUE!
001 502
001 509
001 509
DREDD

HOLD IT, YOU!
AAAH!
NAME: THOMAS ZEDD
AGE: 53
OCCUPATION: FORMER ZOMBIE KEEPER AT AGG BIO.
PRESENT POSITION: BLEEDING TO DEATH ON THE ZOMBIE DORM FLOOR.
FUNNY... WHO'D HAVE THOUGHT THREE SHORT MONTHS AGO THAT ZOMBIES WERE WORTH DYING FOR...!
HE'D BEEN ALL BRIGHT-EYED AND EAGER. 53 YEARS OLD AND HIS FIRST CHANCE AT A JOB. TOMMY ZEDD WASN'T GOING TO LOUSE IT UP.
THIS IS THE MAIN DORM. A LARGE PART OF YOUR TIME WILL BE SPENT HERE, LOOKING AFTER YOUR CHARGES. THEY'RE QUITE INCAPABLE OF DOING ANYTHING FOR THEMSELVES.

WILL WE HAVE TO WEAR THESE SUITS ALL THE TIME, DIRECTOR?
YES. IT'S MOST IMPORTANT THAT OUR OWN BACTERIA DON'T SPREAD CONTAMINATION.
001 509
THIS IS RICK HUDSEN WARD, ONE OF OUR PRIMARY DISEASE UNITS. HERE WE'RE INVESTIGATING THE EFFECTS OF A NEW DRUG ON VARIOUS STAGES OF WRIGLEY'S DISEASE, OR DEADLY THROAT BLOAT AS IT IS COMMONLY KNOWN.
I SEE SOME OF YOU LOOKING SQUEAMISH. DON'T BE. THESE AREN'T HUMANS – THEY'RE GENETICALLY MUTATED LAB ANIMALS, NOTHING MORE.
002 776
ZEDD
JONES
DOESN'T IT HURT THEM?
GOOD QUESTION. THE ANSWER IS NO.
ZEDD
THEIR BRAINS ARE TINY, LARGE ENOUGH ONLY TO PERMIT BASIC MOTOR AND BODILY FUNCTIONS. THEY ARE TOTALLY INSENSITIVE TO PAIN. THEY HAVE NO THOUGHTS, NO FEELINGS, NO PERSONALITY. IN A WORD – ZOMBIES.
002 773
NO. WHO'D HAVE THOUGHT ZOMBIES WERE WORTH DYING FOR? CERTAINLY NOT TOMMY ZEDD, AS HE WENT ABOUT HIS DUTIES...
C'MON, EAT UP, DUMMY!

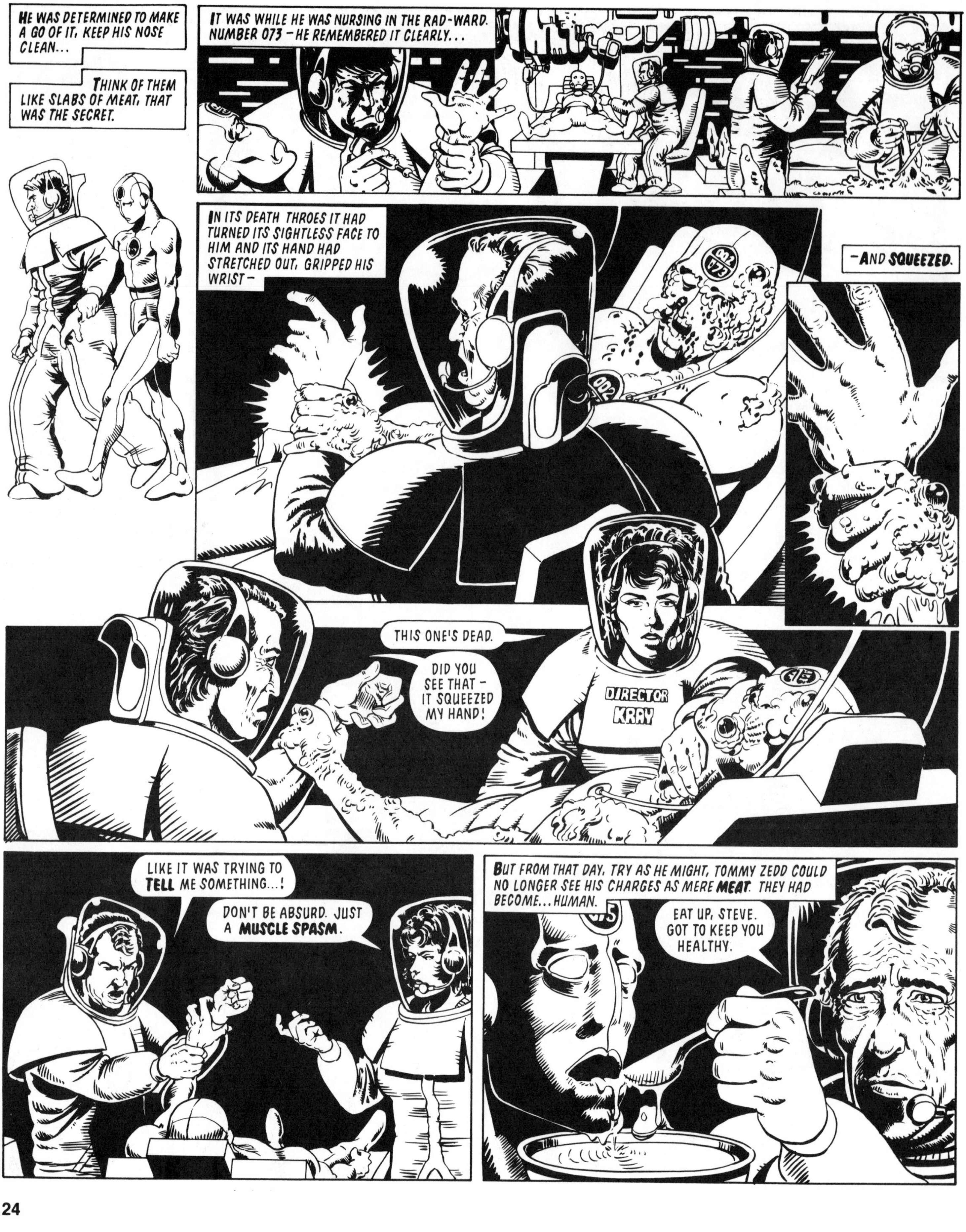

THINK OF THEM LIKE SLABS OF MEAT, THAT WAS THE SECRET.

IT WAS WHILE HE WAS NURSING IN THE RAD-WARD. NUMBER 073 – HE REMEMBERED IT CLEARLY...

IN ITS DEATH THROES IT HAD TURNED ITS SIGHTLESS FACE TO HIM AND ITS HAND HAD STRETCHED OUT, GRIPPED HIS WRIST –

– AND **SQUEEZED**.

THIS ONE'S DEAD.

DID YOU SEE THAT – IT SQUEEZED MY HAND!

DIRECTOR KRAY

HEALTHY FOR WHAT? SO AGG CAN PUMP THEM FULL OF DISEASE! WATCH AND TAKE NOTES AS THEY ROT AWAY!
IT'S NOT RIGHT! IT'S NOT!
AND, INEVITABLY, HIS WORK SUFFERED —
AGG THOUGHT WE WERE DOING THE CITY A FAVOUR, HIRING HUMANS TO DO ROBOTS' WORK. EVIDENTLY WE WERE WRONG.
AGGBIO
YOU'VE ALLOWED YOURSELF TO BECOME EMOTIONALLY INVOLVED WITH YOUR ZOMBIES. I UNDERSTAND YOU'RE EVEN GIVING THEM NAMES NOW.
WELL, WE CAN'T HAVE IT. THAT KIND OF ATTITUDE IS NO USE TO US. YOU'RE FIRED.
DIRECTOR
HE SHOULD HAVE BEEN GLAD TO GET OUT OF THAT TORTURE FACTORY, BUT HIS CONSCIENCE WOULDN'T LET HIM FORGET...
AGG BIO
...WHAT TERRIBLE THINGS WERE THEY DOING TODAY TO DAVE AND STEVE...? WHAT DISEASE WERE THEY INJECTING INTO SIMON — OR GIL — OR BARRIE —?
HE HAD TO RELEASE THEM FROM THIS OBSCENITY. FAR BETTER THEY DIE DECENTLY — QUICKLY.
GOODBYE, YOU GUYS!
SORRY — BUT IT'S THE ONLY WAY!
TROUBLE WAS, TOMMY ZEDD HADN'T FIGURED ON DYING HIMSELF —
GOT TO GET HIM OUT OF HERE...

LUCKY IT'S NIGHT. ONLY ROBOT STAFF ON DUTY.
EMERGENCY SQUADS ARRIVE ON THE SCENE —
FIRE TEAMS! IGNORE THE LAB! JUST MAKE SURE THE FIRE DOESN'T SPREAD!
YOU'RE GOING TO LET IT BURN?
THERE'S HALF A HUNDRED DANGEROUS DISEASES HELD IN THERE. THE ONLY SAFE COURSE IS TO INCINERATE THEM.
HE'S DEAD. NAME'S THOMAS ZEDD — FORMER ZOMBIE KEEPER. AGG GAVE HIM THE BOOT A COUPLE OF DAYS BACK.
SO HE THOUGHT HE'D GET EVEN, HUH?
NO. IT WASN'T THAT.
IT WASN'T THAT AT ALL.
002 508
001 509
THE END.

THE STATUTES OF LIBERTY
$1.60 Malaysia
70c Australia
77c New Zealand (Inc G.S.T.)
88g Mercury
210g Venus
66g Mars
110g Saturn
2g Pluto
429g Neptune
26p EARTH MONEY
2000 AD
FEATURING JUDGE DREDD
PROG 496
15 NOV 86
"GIVE ME YOUR PERPS, YOUR MUTIES, YOUR PSYCHOS..."
...AND I'LL GIVE 'EM HELL!
VOL 2000 THE LAW
THE LAW
DREDD
CLIFF ROBINSON '86.

HEAVY TENSION IN OLD TOWN TONIGHT. THE JUDGES ARE OUT IN FORCE.
OF COURSE, THERE'S ALWAYS TENSION IN OLD TOWN, BUT TONIGHT YOU COULD CUT IT WITH A KNIFE, AND ALL WEEK THERE'S BEEN A BUZZ ON THE STREETS...
"SATURDAY"... "CRIPPEN AND TURK"... "SATURDAY"...
JUDGE
JUDGE DREDD
SCRIPT T.B. GROVER ART ROBINSON LETTERING RICH
TWO STRONG MEN SO EVENLY MATCHED THAT ONLY A FOOL WOULD TRY TO PREDICT THE OUTCOME.
ONE CALLED CRIPPEN. THE OTHER, TURK.
ONE FROM RIDGELEY. ONE FROM MICHAEL.
THEY FACE EACH OTHER, KEYED-UP, NERVOUS - BUT NOT AFRAID. TWO MEN CONFIDENT OF THEIR OWN POWER.

DREDD
ROMERO
THE FIGHT IS TONIGHT, ALL RIGHT. QUESTION IS — WHERE?
THEY MEET IN A RUSTING CHILDREN'S PLAYPIT, WHERE THE STEPPED SLAB FORMS A NATURAL ARENA AND THE WALLS OF THE TWIN TOWERS SHIELD THEM FROM UNWELCOME EYES ...
ANDREW RIDGELEY
CITEMENT CRACKLES THROUGH E GATHERING CROWD LIKE ELECTRICITY.
THEN THE FIRST BLOW IS STRUCK!

HIGH ABOVE OLD TOWN, A JUSTICE DEPT H-WAGON MONITORS —
WE'VE GOT A PATTERN DEVELOPING.
TWO HUNDRED PLUS INDIVIDUALS GATHERED OR CONVERGING ON GRID REF 413/890.
DREDD HERE. WE'LL CHECK IT.
MURGY! QUICK! IT'S THEM! CRIPPEN AND TURK – IT'S STARTED!
WORD SPREADS THROUGH THE TWIN TOWERS —
CRIPPEN FOR RIDGELEY!
TURK! TURK! TURK!
TURK'S DOWN!
FINISH HIM, CRIP!
IN WITH THE BOOT!
KILL HIM! KILL HIM!
CRIPPEN OF RIDGELEY IGNORES THE HOWLING MOB. THIS COMBAT IS NONE OF HIS CHOOSING. IF HE MUST FIGHT, THEN HE'LL DO IT FAIRLY.
SOMEHOW, HE SENSES THE SAME OF TURK.
NO WEAPONS, NO TRICKS.
JUST MAN AGAINST MAN.

AT LEAST THAT WAY THIS SAVAGE BLOCKRITE CAN RETAIN... A KIND OF HONOUR.
THAT'S IT!
HOLD UP, ROMERO.
DREDD TO CONTROL! BLOCK FIGHT IS ON, ABANDONED PLAYPIT OFF WHAM PASSAGE.
SURROUND WHOLE AREA, BUT INSTRUCT UNITS TO MAINTAIN DISTANCE. AWAIT MY CALL.
YOU'RE LETTING THEM FIGHT ON?
ATTABOY, TURKY!
DUMB CRIP! SHOULDA STOMPED THAT PRETTY BOY WHEN YOU HADDA CHANCE!
CRIPPEN FOR RIDGELEY
GET UP, CRIP!
I CAN'T WATCH!
THERE HAD BEEN A LOT OF BAD FEELING BETWEEN RIDGELEY AND MICHAEL, THE TWIN BLOCKS WHICH ALWAYS SEEMED TO BE AT EACH OTHER'S THROATS. IT HAD TO BE SETTLED.
GRUD KNOWS WHAT FACELESS BLOCK COMMITTEE HAD CHOSEN THIS METHOD, OR WHY IT SHOULD BE CRIPPEN AND TURK. THEIR REPUTATIONS AS FIGHTERS? MEN WHO KNEW HOW TO STAND UP FOR THEMSELVES?
BUT SOON EVERY RESIDENT OF THE TWIN TOWERS KNEW. IT HAD BECOME A MATTER OF BLOCK HONOUR. THERE WAS NO BACKING OUT.
CRIPPEN'S GOT GUTS!
TURK'LL TAKE HIM!

AND SO THEY FIGHT, WITH THE WEIGHT OF THEIR BLOCKS RESTING ON THEIR SHOULDERS. MEN OF HONOUR...
STRANGE HOW TWO SUCH AS THEY SHOULD HAVE COME TOGETHER AMIDST THIS SEA OF SAVAGERY.
BUT IN THE END, EVEN AMONG MEN OF HONOUR, THERE MUST BE A VICTOR.

OUT COLD.

FOR BOTH WINNERS AND LOSERS THERE IS A SUDDEN, PALPABLE RELEASE OF TENSION.
CRIPPEN FOR RIDGELEY!

OH! WE'LL NEVER BE ABLE TO LOOK A RIDGELEY IN THE EYE AGAIN!
AT LEAST IT'S OVER, MURGY!

DREDD HERE! YOU'RE CLEAR TO MOVE IN. ARREST THEM ALL!
DREDD

JUDGES!
SCATTER!
BUT THERE IS NO ESCAPE.

YOU OKAY, TURK?
YEAH... RECKON.
TURK WILLIAMSON -- ANTHONY JEDRICK CRIPPEN - I'M SENTENCING YOU TO 18 MONTHS APIECE.
TAKE 'EM AWAY.
WHY DID YOU LET THEM GO ON, DREDD?
BECAUSE IF I'D STOPPED THEM, THE POT WOULD HAVE GONE ON BOILING. THIS WAY THE MATTER'S SETTLED. THERE'LL BE NO MORE TROUBLE BETWEEN GEORGE MICHAEL AND ANDY RIDGELEY - NOT FOR A WHILE, AT LEAST.
DREDD
BESIDES, YOU'RE NEVER TOO OLD TO ENJOY A GOOD FIGHT.
THE END.

PROBABLY THE FINEST LOGO IN THE WORLD...

THE MEGA-TIMES
12 Creds.
NING EDITION
CHIEF
JUDGE
RESIGN
FAREWELL, McGRUDER ! YOUR NAME WILL BE REMEMBERED AS LONG AS JUSTICE ENDURES !
McGRUDER
JUDGE DREDD
SCRIPT T B GROVER
ART CLIFF ROBINSON
LETTERING T FRAME

THE GRAND HALL OF JUSTICE. A MEETING OF THE COUNCIL OF FIVE -
CHIEF JUDGE, WE ASK YOU - RECONSIDER.
HALL OF JUSTICE

YOU MADE AN ERROR OF JUDGEMENT, CERTAINLY.* BUT ONE ERROR IN AN EXEMPLARY CAREER CAN SURELY BE OVERLOOKED.
YES, WE'RE MAKING TOO MUCH OF IT.
AGREED.
SHENKER - YOU WANT YOUR TWO CREDS' WORTH ?
* SEE PROG 455 - THARG.

I THINK YOU'VE MADE THE RIGHT DECISION, CHIEF JUDGE.
WHAT DOES THAT MEAN, SHENKER?
BEING CRYPTIC AS USUAL. IT DOESN'T MATTER. THE VOTE IS CLEAR — YOU MUST STAY, MA'AM.

THEN I OVERRIDE THE VOTE. I HAVE GIVEN THE MATTER DEEP AND CAREFUL CONSIDERATION AND MY DECISION STANDS. I AM NO LONGER COMPETENT TO HOLD THIS OFFICE.
TOMORROW MORNING AT DAWN I WILL TAKE THE LONG WALK INTO THE CURSED EARTH AND LEAVE THIS CITY FOREVER.

MY FINAL ACT AS CHIEF JUDGE IS TO DISMISS CREED, HERPERT AND RENBOW FROM THE COUNCIL OF FIVE.
DISMISSED?

YOUR SUPPORT FOR ME SAYS MUCH FOR YOUR LOYALTY, BUT IT ALSO SHOWS YOUR OWN JUDGEMENT TO BE FLAWED.
YOU WILL UNDERGO FULL PSYCHIATRIC AND OPERATIONAL EVALUATION AND, IF POSSIBLE, BE RETURNED TO NON-EXECUTIVE DUTIES WITHIN YOUR OWN DIVISIONS.
THERE IS, OF COURSE, THE OPTION OF THE LONG WALK. BUT THAT WILL BE YOUR DECISION.

SHENKER, I'LL BE APPOINTING NEW MEMBERS TO JOIN YOU ON THE COUNCIL.
VERY WELL. GOOD LUCK, McGRUDER.

AND JUSTICE DEPARTMENT HAS JUST ANNOUNCED THE NAMES OF FOUR NEW MEMBERS WHO WILL TAKE THEIR PLACES ON THE COUNCIL OF FIVE, THE CITY'S FOREMOST LAWMAKING BODY...

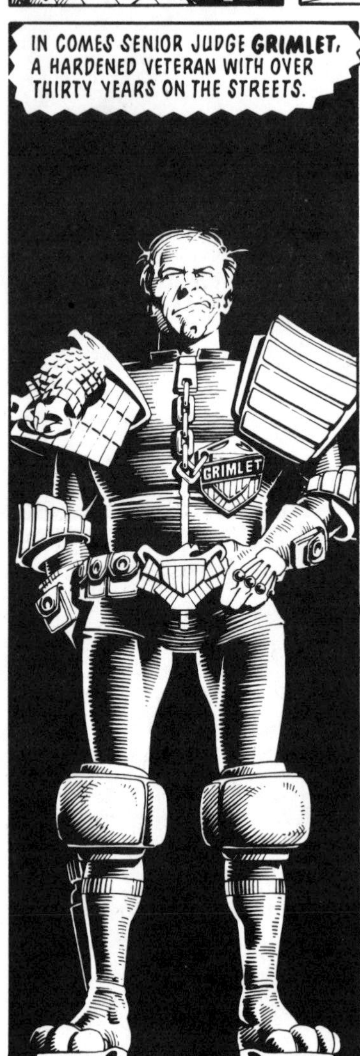
IN COMES SENIOR JUDGE GRIMLET, A HARDENED VETERAN WITH OVER THIRTY YEARS ON THE STREETS.
GRIMLET

JUDGE-TUTOR SILVER, FOR TWELVE YEARS PRINCIPAL LECTURER IN APPLIED VIOLENCE AT THE ACADEMY OF LAW.
SILVER TUTOR

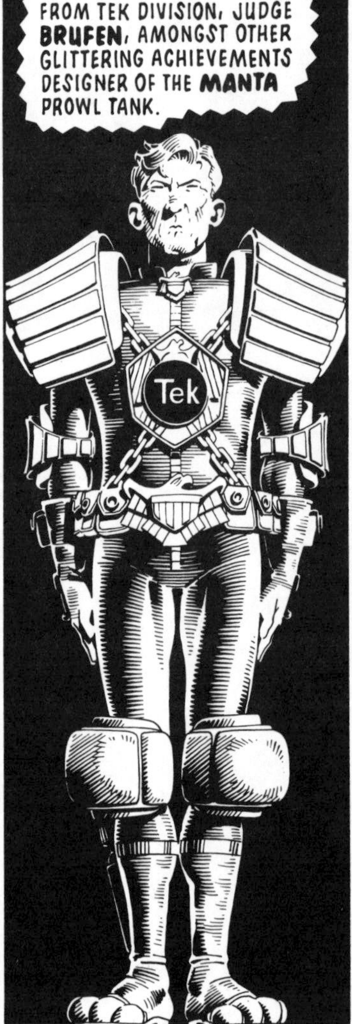
FROM TEK DIVISION, JUDGE BRUFEN, AMONGST OTHER GLITTERING ACHIEVEMENTS DESIGNER OF THE MANTA PROWL TANK.
Tek

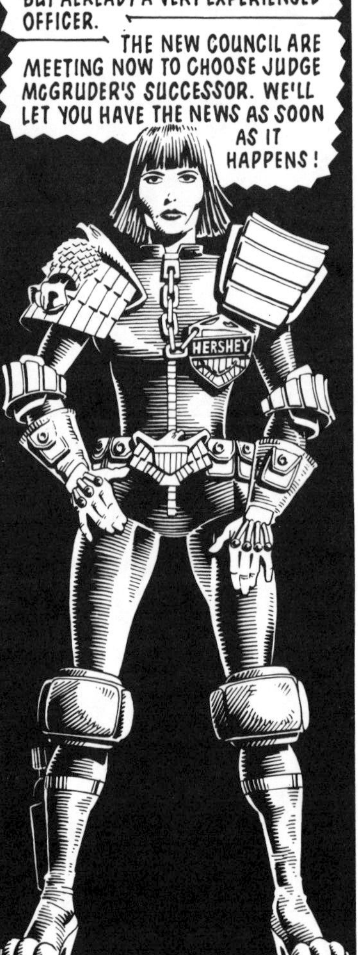
SURPRISE CHOICE FOR THE COUNCIL, JUDGE HERSHEY. YOUNG IN YEARS BUT ALREADY A VERY EXPERIENCED OFFICER.
THE NEW COUNCIL ARE MEETING NOW TO CHOOSE JUDGE McGRUDER'S SUCCESSOR. WE'LL LET YOU HAVE THE NEWS AS SOON AS IT HAPPENS!
HERSHEY

NEW NAMES, NEW FACES! A **FRESH WIND** THROUGH THE COBWEBS OF JUSTICE! PERHAPS A **NEW DEAL** FOR THE PEOPLE – THE FIRST STEP ON THE ROAD TO A FAIRER, MORE **HUMANE** SOCIETY!
YEAH, AN' I'M TWO-TON TONY TUBBS.
YOU THINK I MADE THE RIGHT DECISION, DREDD?
IT'S A QUESTION OF ATTITUDE. IF YOU FELT YOUR EFFICIENCY WAS IMPAIRED, THEN IT WAS. YOU HAD TO GO.
YES.
DREDD
McGRUDER
ANY IDEA WHO THEY'LL CHOOSE TO REPLACE YOU?
ACCORDING TO SHENKER, IT'LL BE SILVER.
"GOOD CHOICE. SILVER'S A HARD MAN. A FAIR MAN... BUT MAINLY A **HARD** MAN.
"HE WON'T SHRINK IF DIFFICULT DECISIONS HAVE TO BE MADE...
"THE PEOPLE WON'T LIKE IT, OF COURSE. THEY KNOW HIS REPUTATION..."
IF THEY DON'T LIKE IT, THEY CAN ALWAYS LUMP IT.
KNOWING SILVER, THEY PROBABLY WILL.
SILVER
TUTOR
TEK
HER

DAWN, NEXT MORNING –
OPEN THE GATES!
IN A WAY, DREDD, IT'S A RELIEF. CHIEF JUDGE – BEFORE THAT SJS – I'VE BEEN COOPED UP TOO LONG.
IT'LL BE GOOD TO SEE SOME ACTION AGAIN.
DREDD
STILL, I'M GOING TO MISS IT.
THEN SHE TURNS AND WALKS THROUGH THE HONOUR GUARD –
FIRE!
McGRUDER

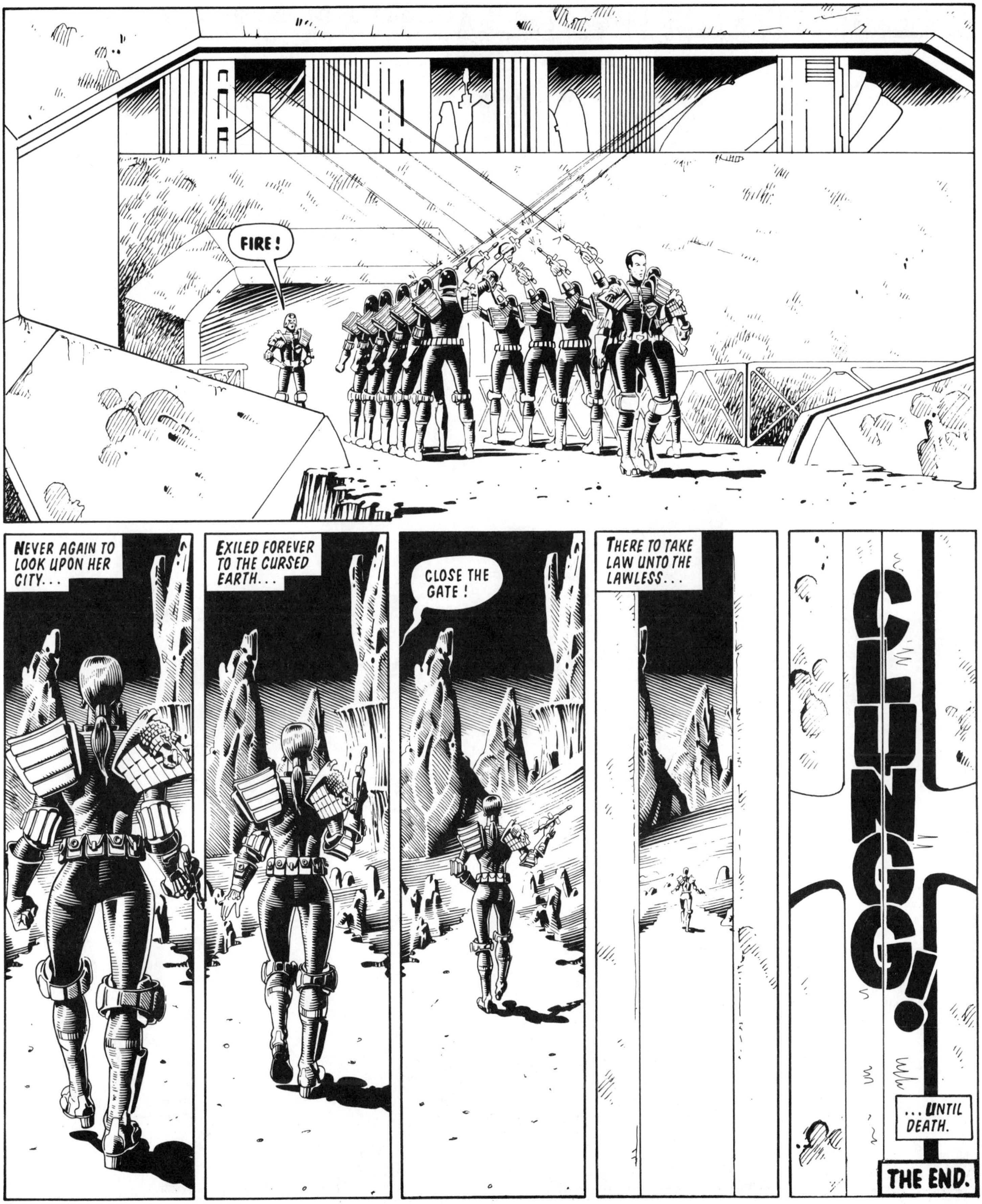

FIRE!

NEVER AGAIN TO LOOK UPON HER CITY...

EXILED FOREVER TO THE CURSED EARTH...

CLOSE THE GATE!

THERE TO TAKE LAW UNTO THE LAWLESS...

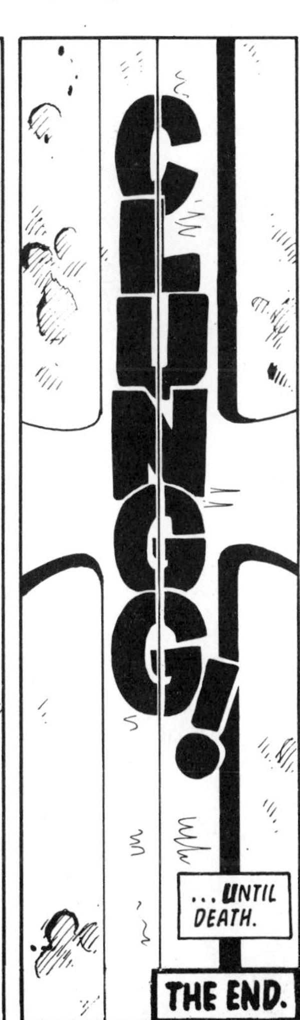
CLUNGG!
...UNTIL DEATH.
THE END.

BREAK THE LAW AND HE'LL BREAK YOU!
$1.70 Malaysia
75c Australia
85c New Zealand (Inc. G.S.T.)
88g Mercury
210g Venus
66g Mars
110g Saturn
2g Pluto
26p EARTH MONEY
PROG 511
28FEB 87
IN ORBIT EVERY MONDAY
2000 AD
FEATURING JUDGE DREDD
DREDD
BELIEVE IT!
CLIFF ROBINSON '87.

JUDGE DREDD
A NEW PIRATE VID CHANNEL MAKES ITS FIRST BROADCAST TO THE MEGA-CITY –
GOOD EVENING AND WELCOME TO CHANNEL ILLEGAL, THE STATION THAT DOESN'T GIVE A HOOT!
I'M YOUR HOST, SID BLITZEN! LET'S GO STRAIGHT TO OUR FIRST – AND PROBABLY LAST – PROGRAMME!
CHANNEL ILLEGAL
BOOBY TRAP
CHANNEL ILLEGAL
YES, IT'S BOOBY TRAP! THE NEW QUIZ GAME THAT'LL SHOCK YOUR PANTS OFF – ESPECIALLY IF YOU HAPPEN TO LIVE IN THE SAME BLOCK AS ONE OF OUR CONTESTANTS!
NOW LET'S MEET THE TWO BOOBS WHO'LL BE PLAYING BOOBY TRAP!
MARVIN SLURRY FROM RAY KROC BLOCK! MARVIN IS AN UNEMPLOYED SPUTUM ANALYST AND HIS HOBBIES ARE MUSCLE-BUILDING AND DONATING BLOOD!
HI!
1 2 3 4 5 6 7 8 9 10
MARVIN SLURRY RAY KROC BLOCK
MARVIN'S OPPONENT, UNCTIOUS WILSON FROM BOB CALVI BLOCK. UNCTIOUS IS A PART-TIME LIAR WITH THE CITY HOUSING DEPT AND HIS HOBBIES INCLUDE BAT GLIDING, FILLING IN FORMS AND WEIGHING THINGS!
HI!
1 2 3 4 5 6 7 8 9 10
UNCTIOUS WILSON BOB CALVI BLOCK
THE RULES ARE SIMPLE! BEHIND EACH CONTESTANT ARE TEN NUMBERS, EACH REPRESENTING A BOOBY TRAP PLANTED BY ME IN THEIR BLOCKS.
EACH PLAYER MUST SET OFF ALL HIS OPPONENT'S BOOBY TRAPS BEFORE HIS OWN – THEREBY MAKING HIS OPPONENT'S BLOCK A THOROUGHLY UNPLEASANT PLACE TO BE! HA, HA!
BUT THERE'S A CATCH! BEWARE THE BOOBY NUMBER!
YES, PLAYERS! ONE OF YOUR OPPONENT'S NUMBERS WILL ACTIVATE A FLESH-DISINTEGRATOR PLANTED BENEATH YOUR OWN SEAT!
SCRIPT T.B. GROVER
ART C. ROBINSON
LETTERING T. FRAME
DROKK IT! THE PERP'S FALLING...

HUH? YOU NEVER SAID NOTHIN' ABOUT NO **FLESH DISINTEGRATOR**!
DOOM TRAP
YOU CAN SHOVE IT, SID! I'M QUITTIN'!
DON'T MOVE, UNCTIOUS!
I FORGOT TO MENTION – THE FLESH DISINTEGRATORS ARE ALSO PRIMED TO ACTIVATE IF YOU EVEN ATTEMPT TO RISE FROM YOUR SEAT!
ULP!
SO STRAIGHT AWAY IT'S THE FIRST QUESTION TO MARVIN!
MARVIN – WHO WROTE THE IMMORTAL CLASSIC "MOBY DICK"?
LESSEE... IT WAS EITHER ETHEL MERMAN OR HERMAN MELVILLE... OR WAS IT ETHEL MELVILLE?
NO! I KNOW! IT WAS **HERMAN MERMAN**!
THAT'S CLOSE ENOUGH, MARVIN! CHOOSE YOUR **FIRST NUMBER**!
1
2
3
4
5
6
7
8
9
10
UH, **4**, SID.
NUMBER **4** IT IS!
UNCTIOUS WILSON
YOU'VE CHOSEN A **NASTY** ONE FOR UNCTIOUS, MARVIN! IT'S AN OBNOXIOUS **STINK BOMB** LOCATED IN APARTMENT **39F** OF HIS BLOCK!
4
AND IN BOB CALVI BLOCK –
APARTMENT 39F... HEY, THAT'S **US**!
I THOUGHT **SID BLITZEN** LOOKED FAMILIAR – JUST LIKE THAT REPAIRMAN WHO CALLED THIS MORNING.
HE LEFT HIS TOOL KIT BEHIND.

EACH BOOBY TRAP WILL BE DETONATED BY REMOTE CONTROL! SO WITHOUT FURTHER ADO —
— IT'S FUN TIMMME!
BLLAARRT!
EEUUUGH! THAT STENCH!
FEEL SICK! RUN FOR IT!
MOLEY! WHAT A SMELL!
NICE ONE, MARV! THAT PONG WILL LAST FOR YEARS!
NEXT QUESTION GOES TO YOU, UNCTIOUS.
TOOLS
IN A JUSTICE DEPT MONITORING STATION, JUDGES PICK UP THE ILLEGAL BROADCAST —
THAT'S CORRECT, UNCTIOUS! CHOOSE YOUR NUMBER!
IS THIS SHOW FOR REAL?
BETTER GET JUDGES TO THOSE TWO BLOCKS TO CHECK IT OUT.
FOX
UNCTIOUS HAS CHOSEN NUMBER 7 — AND IT'S A BEAUT! IT'S A MASSIVE ITCHING POWDER BOMB IN MARVIN'S BLOCK SHOPPING MALL!
7
IT'S FUN TIME!
AND IN RAY KROC BLOCK SHOPPING MALL —
FADOOMPH!
WHAT THE DEVIL — ?
LITTER

ITCHING POWDER!
AHHHH!
SCRATCH ME! SCRATCH ME!
WE'VE LOCATED THE SOURCE OF THE SIGNALS, IN SECTOR 133! THE SOURCE IS MOBILE — CURRENTLY MOVING ALONG THE ORWELL LOOP!
ATTENTION ANY JUDGE VICINITY ORWELL LOOP — INTERCEPT THAT PIRATE OPERATION!
DREDD HERE! ON THE ORWELL FEEDWAY. I'LL TAKE IT!
DREDD
WEEAAOOWEEOW
VROOM
MARVIN — WHAT IS THE NAME OF THE CITY'S PRESENT MAYOR?
THAT'S AN EASY ONE, SID! DAVE THE ORANG UTAN, OF COURSE.
CORRECT! CHOOSE YOUR NUMBER!
9
NUMBER 9! THAT'S A SMALL DETONATOR CONCEALED IN THE CALVI BLOCK WATER PIPES!
IT'S FUN TIME! HA, HA!
BLAMM
SWOOOSH!

HEY! WATER COMIN' UNDER THE DOOR!
MUST BE A LEAK!
MAINTENANCE
SKOOOSH!
AAAAAAAAH!
JUDGES ARRIVE AT THE TWO BLOCKS –
DROKK! RESPIRATOR DOWN!
BLUUUUH!
COUGH COUGH!
ELKIN HERE – AT CALVI! THE WHOLE 37TH FLOOR HERE STINKS LIKE NOTHING ON EARTH! PEOPLE ARE RUNNING FOR THE STAIRS –
ELKIN
OH MOLEY! FLASH FLOOD!

AAAGHHHH!
BOOBY TRAP NUMBER 2 FOR UNCTIOUS – AND IT'S SMOKE CANISTERS IN THE VENTILATION DUCTS!
2
CHUNG HERE – KROC MALL! WE'RE GONNA NEED MED-SQUADS! TELL 'EM TO BRING PLENTY OF CALAMINE!
FSSSS!
NOT TO MENTION SMOKE EXTRACTORS!
THINK I GOT YOUR PIRATE LOCATED, CONTROL. BIG TRANSPORTER, HEADING OFF THE LOOP INTO BLAIR BOULEVARD!
IT'S ON AUTOMATIC PILOT!
BIKE – MAINTAIN POSITION!

I'M GOING ABOARD!
MARVIN – IF IT TAKES EIGHT MEN THREE HOURS TO DIG A DITCH, WHY DIDN'T THEY GET ROBOTS TO DIG IT?
GUESS THEY JUST WEREN'T AVAILABLE, SID!
THAT'LL DO NICELY!
6
7
8
9
10
I'LL TAKE NUMBER 1!
NUMBER 1 – THAT'S THE FOAM!
GOTTA PARK THIS THING!
SCREEEEEEE!
IN CALVI BLOCK POOL –
FWOOMPH!
YIKES!
MUST BE BATH NIGHT IN CALVI!
THE POOL'S FOAMING UP!
RUN!

OUR SHOW SEEMS TO BE RUNNING OUT OF TIME! UNCTIOUS-LAST QUESTION! IN WHAT YEAR DID NEVILLE FRIGBY SET THE WORLD TOOTH PULLING RECORD?
1914!
WRONG! I CAN OFFER THAT TO MARVIN!
IT WAS 2093, SID!
THAT'S RIGHT! AND IT'S YOUR TURN TO CHOOSE THE LAST NUMBER!
BLAST - REAR DOOR'S ARMOURED! EVEN HIGH EXPLOSIVE WON'T OPEN IT!
BADAAM!
AND MARVIN'S CHOSEN NUMBER 5 AND IT'S... OH DEAR!
I'M TERRIBLY SORRY, MARVIN, BUT YOU'VE GOT THE BOOBY NUMBER!
5
CLIK!
SO WITHOUT FURTHER ADO, IT'S GOODBYE TIME!
BIKE CANNON - BLOW THIS TIN CAN OPEN!
FZZZZ
FATOOOM!

OKAY, CREEP — THE SHOW'S OVER!
YOU HEARD THE JUDGE, VIDDERS! THIS IS CHANNEL ILLEGAL GOING OFF THE AIR!
SO IT'S GOODBYE FROM HIM —
CHANNEL ILLEGAL
AND GOODBYE FROM ME!
EJECT
SPROING!
CRAAAAAK!
ONE OF THE HAZARDS OF PARKING UNDER A VIADUCT!
THE SHOW'S OVER, JUDGE! I'VE WON! I'M SAFE!

CLIKK!
HOLY CREMOLA! I FORGOT — THE FLESH DISINTEGRATOR!
FZZAK!
DROKK!
THE BOOBY TRAP GAME LEAVES NO WINNERS.
MARVIN SLURRY
THE BUSINESS OF REPAIRING THE DAMAGED BLOCKS WOULD TAKE DAYS...
MEANWHILE -
WHAT A MESS!
CRAZY! WHY DID HE DO IT, DREDD?
SEARCH ME. LOOKIN' FOR A BRIEF HOUR OF FAME, MAYBE - A GREAT PRACTICAL JOKE ON THE CITY, THEN AWAY FREE.
MEDIC
DREDD
CREEP DIDN'T FIGURE ON COLLECTING THE BOOBY PRIZE!
THE END.
KER-SPLUDGE!

CARELESS DRIVING COSTS LIVES

Issued by Justice Dept. Traffic Division in the interests of road safety.

FIRST, WE NEED SNOW.
OKAY, IT'S MEGA-CITY ONE – THEY CONTROL THE WEATHER. BUT IT WOULDN'T BE A REAL CHRISTMAS STORY WITHOUT SNOW, WOULD IT? SO–
–CUE FREAK SNOWSTORM BLOWING IN OVER THE NORTH WALL...
JUDGE DREDD
JUDGE
WEATHER CONTROL! WE GOT A BLIZZARD HERE! CAN'T YOU DO SOMETHING?
WAGNER/GRANT
C. ROBINSON
T. FRAME
DREDD

GATIVE AT THIS TIME. TEM MALFUNCTION. WE'LL YOU KNOW AS AND WHEN.
RIGHT, LET US NOT DILLY-DALLY. BRING ON THE VILLAIN –
MERRY CHRISTMAS! MERRY CHRISTMAS!
CHRISTMAS IS A SPECIAL TIME FOR BILL HUDNUT. A KINDLY, GENEROUS MAN, THERE'S NOTHING BILL LIKES BETTER THAN DRESSING UP AS SANTA AND DISTRIBUTING HARMLESS CONFECTIONS TO ALL THE CITY WAIFS –
HO HO HO, SONNY.
HO HO HO, BILL.
HO-HO-HOLD IT! DID WE SAY VILLAIN?
B-O-R-I-N-G!
WE'VE GOT TO PEP YOU UP A BIT, BILL. HOW ABOUT A GRUESOME STEEL CLAW...?
HUH?
Ping!
AND HOW ABOUT A GLASS PLATE IN HIS HEAD SO YOU CAN SEE HIS BRAIN SLOSHING ABOUT...?
EH?
Ping!

I DO!
GRRRRRRRR

I HATE CHRISTMAS!
BLAM!
BLAM!
OH!
AAAH!
SHATTA!
CALL THE JUDGES!
CONTROL TO DREDD! WE HAVE A CITIZEN AMOK, SHOPPING SPRAWL ON 18TH.
HOLDING POST 5
ON MY WAY!
SO FAR SO GOOD. BUT WAIT-! SOMETHING'S MISSING...
WHERE'S THE EMOTION - THE OLD TUG ON THE HEARTSTRINGS...?
WHERE'S THE LOVE INTEREST?
INTRO JULIET BOUVIER - TALL, SLIM, BLONDE AND BEAUTIFUL...
NO. SCRUB THAT. STEREOTYPE.
Ping!
Ping!
Ping!
INTRO JULIET BOO - SHORT, SPLIT ENDS AND SPOTS - BUT WITH A GOOD HEART, BRIM FULL OF LOVE FOR BILL HUDNUT...

SHE AND BILL HAVE ARRANGED TO MEET UP AT THE SPRAWL FOR SOME LATE NIGHT XMAS SHOPPING...

GRAHH!

B-BILL?

JULIET...?

WH-WHAT'S HAPPENED TO YOU? Y-YOUR ARM-

YOUR **HEAD** -

I CAN SEE YOUR BRAIN... SORT OF... SLOSHING ABOUT.

DON'T MENTION THAT WORD TO ME! I HATE CHRISTMAS!
FADAM! FADAM!
FADADA!
AAH!
B-B-BILL...
A POIGNANT MOMENT. CAN THEIR LOVE SURVIVE THIS UNEXPECTED CRISIS?
ENTER DREDD...
CLEAR THE WAY!
...BEARING FESTIVE CHEER...
YOU DEAF, CITIZEN?
YOU PEOPLE WITH YOUR SMILES AND YOUR HAPPY FACES! YOU MAKE ME SICK! DO ANY OF YOU KNOW WHAT IT'S LIKE TO BE A RAVING PSYCHO?
I DO!
JOHN CARLISLE RAVING PSYCHOS

FADAM!
SHADDUP!
BADAM!
AGGH!
BILL!
DROP IT OR DIE, CREEP!
NO!
JULIET, SWEET JULIET - SPLIT OF ENDS BUT TRUE OF HEART - STAGGERS TOWARDS HER MAN...
YOU'RE BLOCKING MY LINE OF FIRE, WOMAN!

OH, BILL!
PLEASE DON'T DIE! I...I LOVE YOU!
YOU...LOVE ME? EVEN...EVEN AFTER ALL I'VE DONE?
YOU COULDN'T HELP YOURSELF. SOMETHING HAPPENED TO US TONIGHT. SOMETHING WE... WE DON'T UNDERSTAND...
AND BESIDES...IT-IT'S THE SEASON FOR FORGIVING. AFTER ALL, IT'S... CHRISTMAS.
I TOLD YOU, DON'T MENTION THAT WORD!
FADAM!
FADAM!
CRUMPP!
AAAHHH!

CRRUMPPP!

NAMES WERE **BILL HUDNUT** AND **JULIET BOUVIER**. LIVED NEXT DOOR TO EACH OTHER IN **SID VICIOUS**. DUE TO BE MARRIED ON CHRISTMAS DAY.

WHY SHOULD HE SUDDENLY GO OFF THE RAILS? IT DOESN'T MAKE ANY SENSE.
A LOT OF THINGS DON'T MAKE SENSE– LIKE WHERE HE GOT THE **CLAW** AND WHO TURNED HIS HEAD INTO A **FISH TANK**–
AND WHY SHE DOESN'T LOOK ANYTHING **LIKE** JULIET BOUVIER.

LET ME KNOW WHEN YOU FIND OUT THE ANSWERS.
CONTROL! WHEN ARE WE GOING TO GET SOME ACTION ON THIS **WEATHER**?

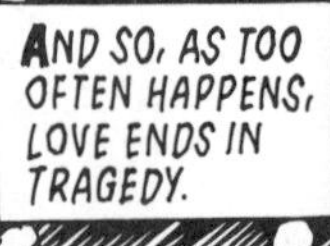
AND SO, AS TOO OFTEN HAPPENS, LOVE ENDS IN TRAGEDY.
HOWEVER, THIS BEING A **CHRISTMAS STORY**, WE MAY TAKE CERTAIN LIBERTIES TO ENSURE A HAPPY ENDING –

THAT IS WHY, ON THE WAY TO THE MORGUE, BILL AND JULIET MIRACULOUSLY RETURN TO LIFE...
Ping!
Ping!
NORRIS

TOTALLY UNNOTICED BY THE ATTENDANT JUDGE, THEY TURN INTO VAPOUR CLOUDS AND SEEP OUT THROUGH A CHINK IN THE DOORS...

OUTSIDE, ANOTHER MIRACLE – THEY REFORM IN THEIR ORIGINAL PERSONALITIES...
AND IF THAT ISN'T MIRACULOUS ENOUGH FOR YOU, JUSTICE DEPT. FORGET THEY EVER EXISTED. THEY RETURN TO THEIR FORMER LIVES AND ON CHRISTMAS DAY THEY ARE JOINED IN MUNICIPAL MATRIMONY.
AND THEY LIVE HAPPILY EVER AFTER.
JUDGE DREDD SPENDS THE REST OF THAT PATROL DISPENSING GOODWILL AMONGST THE CITIZENRY –
JUDGE DREDD! I WANNA CONFESS!
DREDD
NOT TONIGHT, SONNY.
Pat! Pat!
AND A MERRY CHRISTMAS TO YOU, TOO.
DREDD
HO HO HO!

DREDD
CLIFF ROBINSON '86